Contents

Bulletin Board Ideas 6
Learning Center Ideas 7
Pretest 8
Discoveries and Inventions 9
Handy Hints for Inventors 10
Variations on a Theme 11
Why Invent? 12
Combining Parts 13
Rearranging Parts 14
International Inventors Special Service Award 15
Nontechnical Inventions 16
Leonardo da Vinci 17
Construct a Contraption 18
Electronic Braces 19
An Artificial Heart 20
A Quick, Safe Exit 21
Using the Oceans 22
What is a Quagga? 23
The Black Hole Express 24
Two Inventions That Changed a Sport 25
Adventure in Inner Space 26
Sack-a-Snack 27
Choosing to Chew 28
An Effervescent Invention 29
Architectural Inventing 30
Invent a Game 31
Inventors 32
The Cone Connection 33
Intriguing Inventions 34
Protect Your Ideas 35
Correlated Activities 36–37
Posttest 38
Answer Key 39
Ingenious Inventor Award 40

Introduction

Inventions and discoveries change the way people live, and these changes have never been more evident than they are now. More new things have been discovered and invented in the past one hundred years than in all of the centuries that went before. It has been said that half of today's products will be obsolete in five years. We dream of better ways to make and do things. Our dreams become inventions of the future, and through our inventing we are able to solve the seemingly insoluble problems we face today. The activities in this book are designed to (1) introduce students to the creative process which makes discovery and invention possible; (2) highlight a broad range of discoveries and inventions; and (3) encourage innovation, dreaming, and inventing.

Within this book are bulletin board and learning center ideas, a pretest and a posttest, activity pages, a reproducible student record sheet to help you keep track of the pages your students have completed, suggestions for additional correlated activities, an answer key, and an award to be given to students who satisfactorily complete the unit of study. These materials may be used with your entire class, for small-group instruction, or by individuals working independently at their desks or at learning centers. Although you may want to elaborate on the information presented, each activity has been described so that students can do it without additional instruction.

Student Record Sheet

Pages Completed / Students' Names																		

Bulletin Board Ideas

INVENTION TIME LINE

1,750,000 B.C.	flint tools
5000 B.C.	plow
3000 B.C.	wheel
3000 B.C.	writing (by the Sumerians)
A.D. 105	paper (in China)
A.D. 1100	magnetic compass
c. A.D. 1437	printing from movable type
A.D. 1608	telescope
A.D. 1642	adding machine
A.D. 1784	bifocal lens
A.D. 1793	cotton gin
A.D. 1827	friction match
A.D. 1837	magnetic telegraph
A.D. 1852	power elevator
A.D. 1867	typewriter
A.D. 1876	telephone
A.D. 1877	phonograph
A.D. 1888	ballpoint pen
A.D. 1903	first successful powered flight of heavier-than-air vehicle
A.D. 1929	FM radio

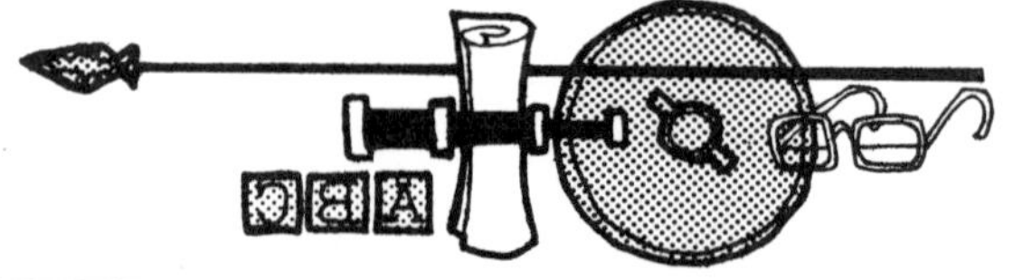

BRIGHT IDEAS by Thomas Alva Edison

★ alkaline storage battery
★ cement mixer
★ dictaphone
★ incandescent electric lamp
★ microphone
★ mimeograph machine
★ motion picture device
★ phonograph
★ stock ticker
★ telephone transmitter
★ vote recorder

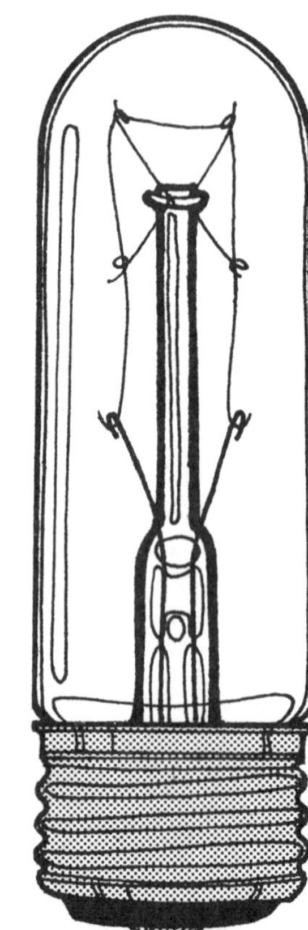

How have these Edison inventions changed our lives?

Learning Center Ideas

Problem-Solving Products

Instructions

1. Choose a problem from the list posted below.
2. Invent a device to help solve this problem.
3. Draw and label a diagram of your invention.
4. Create a television commercial or newspaper advertisement to sell your problem-solving product.

Problems

crime
disease
litter
pollution
poverty
war

Design a Desk

Redesign your desk to make it one any student would love to own and use!

Instructions

1. Examine your school desk carefully.
2. Think of ways you could make it more efficient and more comfortable.
3. Think of features you might add, such as additional storage space, a headrest, or a soft drink dispenser.
4. Redesign your desk to incorporate some of these features.
5. Draw and label a diagram or blueprint of your desk design.

Select ten to twenty common, but perhaps unfamiliar, kitchen and household gadgets. For example, you might include an apple corer, a cheese plane, an egg slicer, an icing syringe, a lemon press, a meat mallet, a pastry blender, a peeler, a rotary beater, a steamer basket, and/or a tea ball. Attach different numbers to these gadgets and place them in a box, bucket, or other similar container. Make the container available on a table or desk in your classroom. Challenge students to identify each gadget by number, name, and use. As a variation, place antique or out-of-date gadgets in the container or have students dream up uncommon uses for the common gadgets.

Ingenious Inventions

The inventions in this box may be unfamiliar to you. Can you figure out how each one is used?

1. Take an answer sheet.
2. Write your name at the top.
3. Examine each object carefully.
4. Describe its purpose or function on the line beside the corresponding number.
5. Place your finished answer sheet in the envelope.

Name ____________________

Pretest

Circle the correct letter.

1. **Invention** is the creation of something that
   a. is unique. c. already exists.
   b. is powerful. d. is expensive.

2. Which one of the following things is a real invention?
   a. ax c. electricity
   b. lightning d. helium

3. The Renaissance inventor who was an artist, engineer, architect, and mathematician was named
   a. Thomas Alva Edison. c. George Washington Carver.
   b. Leonardo da Vinci. d. Alexander Graham Bell.

4. The cartoonist who poked fun at new inventions was named
   a. Charles M. Schulz. c. Thomas Nast.
   b. Rube Goldberg. d. James Thurber.

5. In 1982, the first artificial heart was successfully implanted in the chest of
   a. Christiaan Barnard. c. Barney Clark.
   b. Michael DeBakey. d. Emmanuel Vitria.

6. Another name for the process of harvesting ocean kelp is
   a. plowsharing. c. geoscience.
   b. oceanography. d. aquaculture.

7. The **quagga** is
   a. an extinct animal. c. an early invention.
   b. similar to a supernova. d. a recent discovery.

8. To think like an inventor, you must be willing to
   a. try only one idea or solution and stick with it.
   b. travel to Washington, D.C.
   c. make lots of mistakes without becoming discouraged.
   d. apply for a patent.

9. The best way to increase your creativity is to
   a. obtain a copyright.
   b. enroll in a scientific seminar.
   c. try many variations of an idea.
   d. quickly discard unsuccessful ideas.

10. To protect your inventions, you should obtain
    a. court orders. c. copyrights.
    b. patents. d. trademarks.

Name ______________________

Discoveries and Inventions

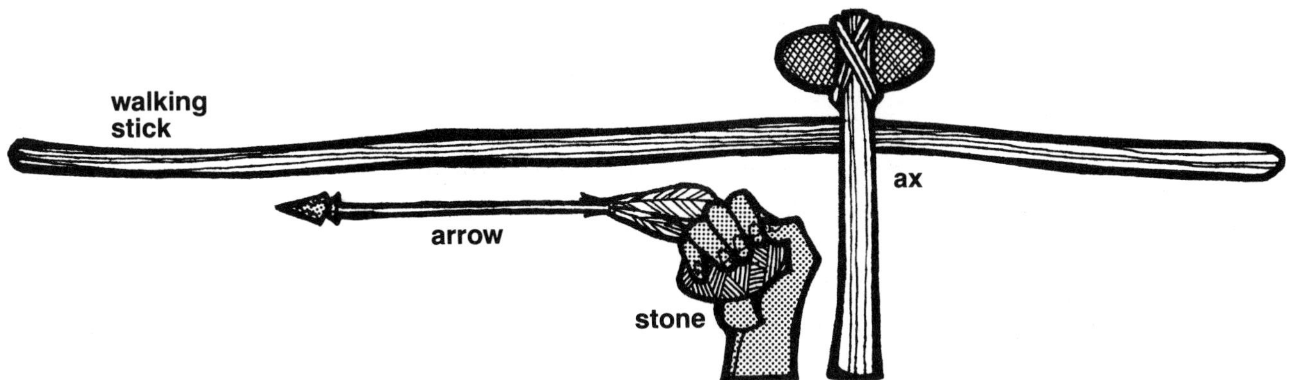

Of these primitive tools our ancestors used, only two can be classified as inventions. The other two are discoveries. Can you figure out which two are which?

Discoveries are things already in existence but learned of for the first time. Discoveries are often made to fulfill a need or to make a task easier. For example, long ago people discovered that it was more effective to hit an animal with a rock than with a fist and that a simple stick could make walking for long distances or over rough terrain a bit easier.

Inventions are things that did not exist and have been created for the first time. The arrow and the ax are inventions. They were based on earlier discoveries and made of available raw materials, but they were new. They had never existed before.

Activities

1. Indicate which ones of the things listed on the chart below are discoveries and which ones are inventions by putting check marks (✓) in the appropriate boxes.

	Discovery	Invention
1. wrapping in skins for warmth		
2. digging stick		
3. electricity		
4. new galaxy		
5. new species of insect		
6. plow		
7. sewing leather to make clothing		

2. Before the invention of the wheel came the discovery that round objects could be rolled and, in this way, moved more easily than flat-sided ones. Make a list of subsequent inventions that have been based on the wheel.

3. Think of an entirely new use for the wheel and describe it in words or labeled pictures.

Name ____________________

Handy Hints for Inventors

From the development of agriculture through the Industrial Revolution and on into the Space Age, inventors have dramatically changed our way of life. Inventors seem to have a "magical" ability to come up with unique ideas, but the secret ingredient in their inventiveness is not magic. Inventors draw upon past discoveries, their own observations and experiences, and their special skills and abilities to come up with ideas that really work.

How can you develop this inventive ability? Some inventors advise that you not be afraid of making mistakes and that you keep on trying even when you fail. Other inventors recommend that you develop your own curiosity and "dream of things that never were."

To Think Like an Inventor

1. Look at a familiar object, but try to see it in a new and different way. Consider ways in which that object might be changed to make an improved version or to create something entirely new.
2. Consider *enlarging* or *reducing* a part of the object.
3. *Rearrange* or *eliminate* some of the parts.
4. *Add on* or *combine* existing parts in new or unusual ways.
5. *Reverse* or *exchange* some of the parts.
6. *Substitute* one part for something else or *substitute* something else for one of the parts.

Activity

Choose a common item (for example, a toaster, a television set, or a telephone), and use one or more of the hints above to turn that item into a brand-new invention. On a separate sheet of paper, draw and label a diagram of your invention. Then write a paragraph in which you describe how it works.

Name ________________________

Variations on a Theme

In how many different ways can you write the letters of the alphabet? Below you see the letter **R** written twenty different ways. In the spaces remaining, write your own variations of this letter.

Being able to think of variations on a theme can increase your creativity. In fact, some scientists and inventors believe that this mental agility is the key to a good imagination and to the ability to find new solutions to old problems and new expressions for old ideas. In the fields of dance, music, and art, for example, new works are created by varying existing themes and popular forms of presentation. Many ballet companies perform their own versions of the *Nutcracker* to music originally written by the Russian composer Tchaikovsky during the nineteenth century. Paganini and Beethoven wrote many musical scores in which they first established a theme and then created variations on it. And Picasso repeatedly painted harlequin figures in a variety of styles ranging from romantic realism to analytical cubism.

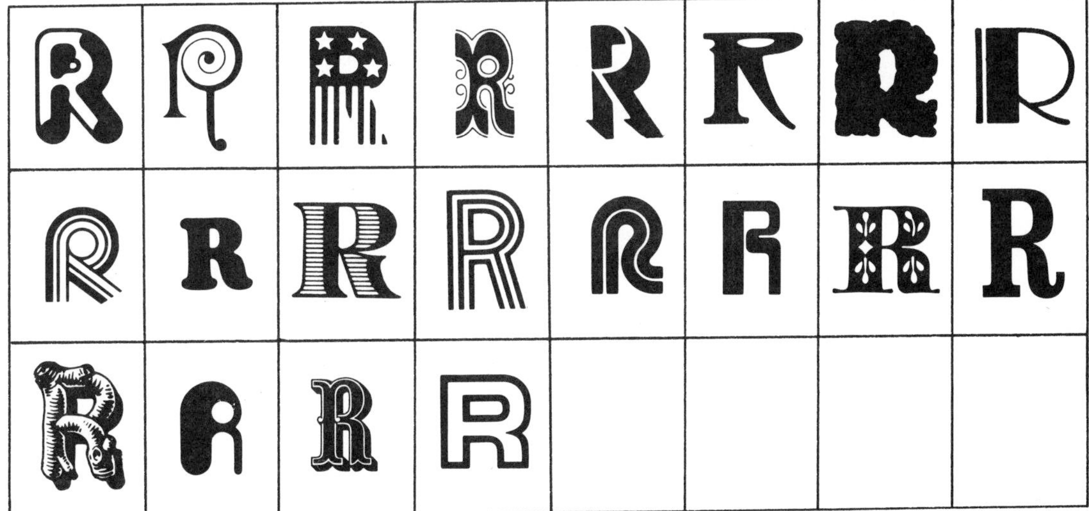

Activity

Think up some new variations on these old themes. Describe your variations in the appropriate boxes of the table below.

Theme	Old Variations	Your New Variations
vanilla ice cream	chocolate chip hot fudge sundae	
roller skate	shoe skate scooter skateboard	

Name ______________________

Why Invent?

Most inventions are created to improve conditions, to solve problems, or to fill needs. On the lines below, list some **improvements** that would benefit your school.

____

____

____

____

____

____

What are some major world **problems** that deserve attention?

____

____

____

List several **needs** of your own that you feel are important.

____

____

____

Choose one improvement, problem, or need and elaborate on it by dreaming up an invention and completing the chart below.

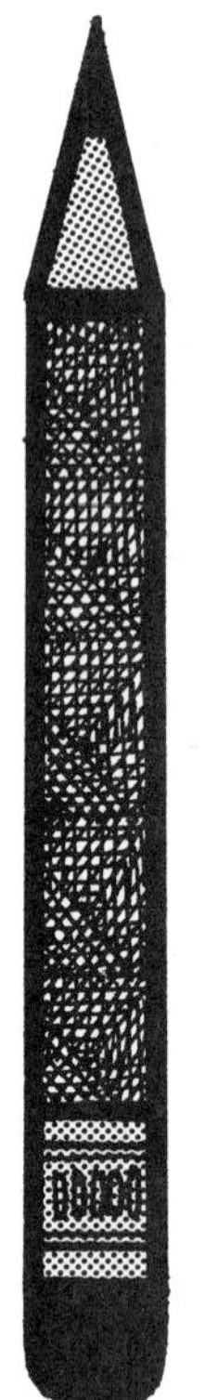

Improvement, problem, or need: ______________________

____

Name of invention: ______________________

Description or sketch of invention:

Projected price: ______________________

This invention would appeal to ______________________

______________________.

In what ways might this improvement, problem, or need be different one hundred years from now?

____

Name ______________________

Combining Parts

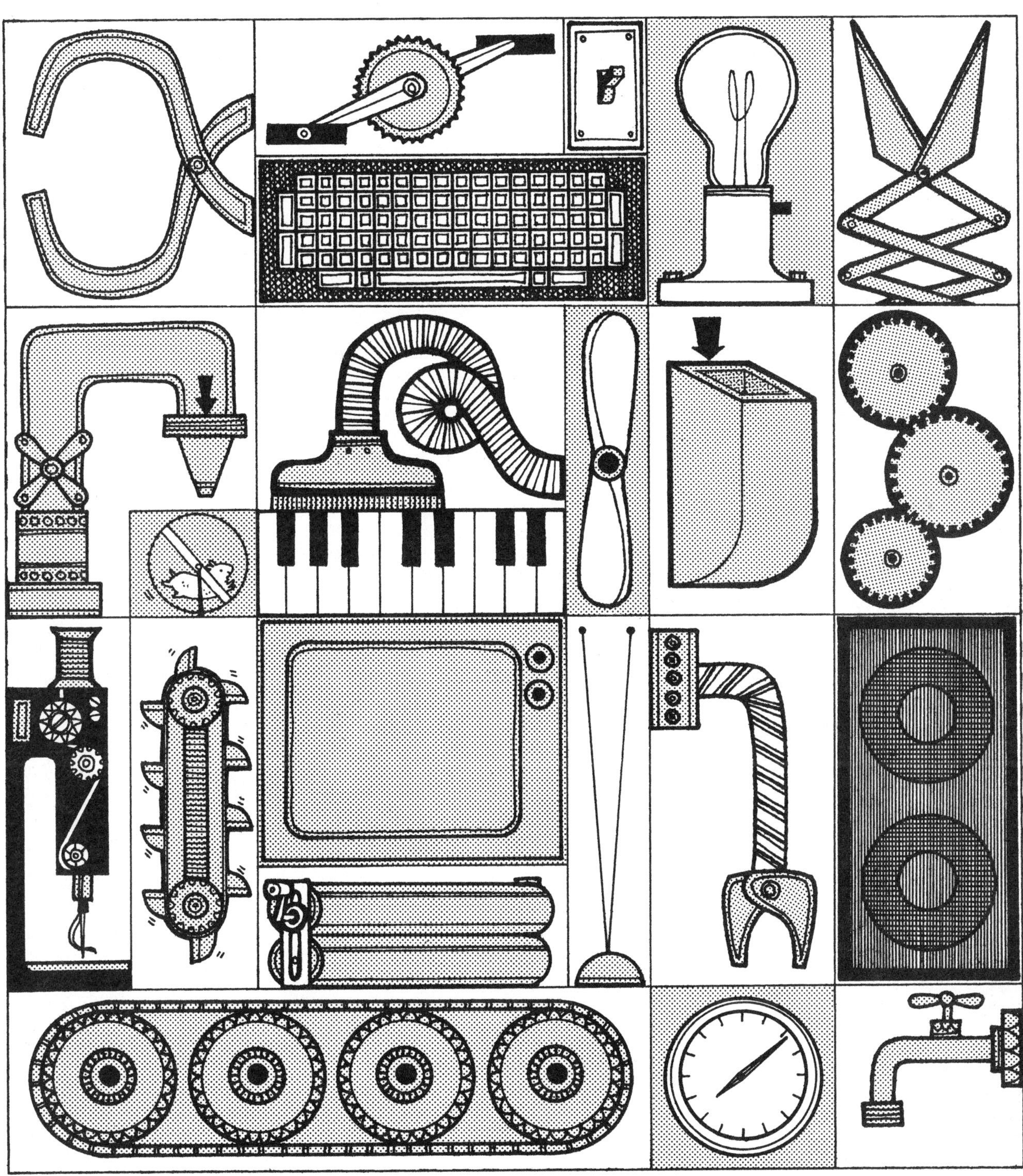

Invent something new by combining two or more of the objects pictured above to form an unusual product. Cut out the parts you will use, and glue them to another piece of paper. Draw lines to connect them and form your invention. You may add parts not pictured. Label your invention. In your own words, list the unique features of your invention and describe how it works. Then explain who will use it and how it is better than other similar inventions.

Name ______________________

Rearranging Parts

Cut out the large vehicle pictured below. Then cut along the dark outlines to separate the vehicle parts. Rearrange these parts to create a new vehicle. When you are satisfied with your arrangement, glue the parts on a sheet of paper. Cut out the label at the bottom of this page. On it, write the name of your vehicle and its purpose. Then compare your new vehicle with the original one. In what ways is your design different? Is it an improvement? What advantages does it offer? Record the results of your vehicle comparison on the label, and glue this label to the sheet of paper on which your new vehicle is pictured.

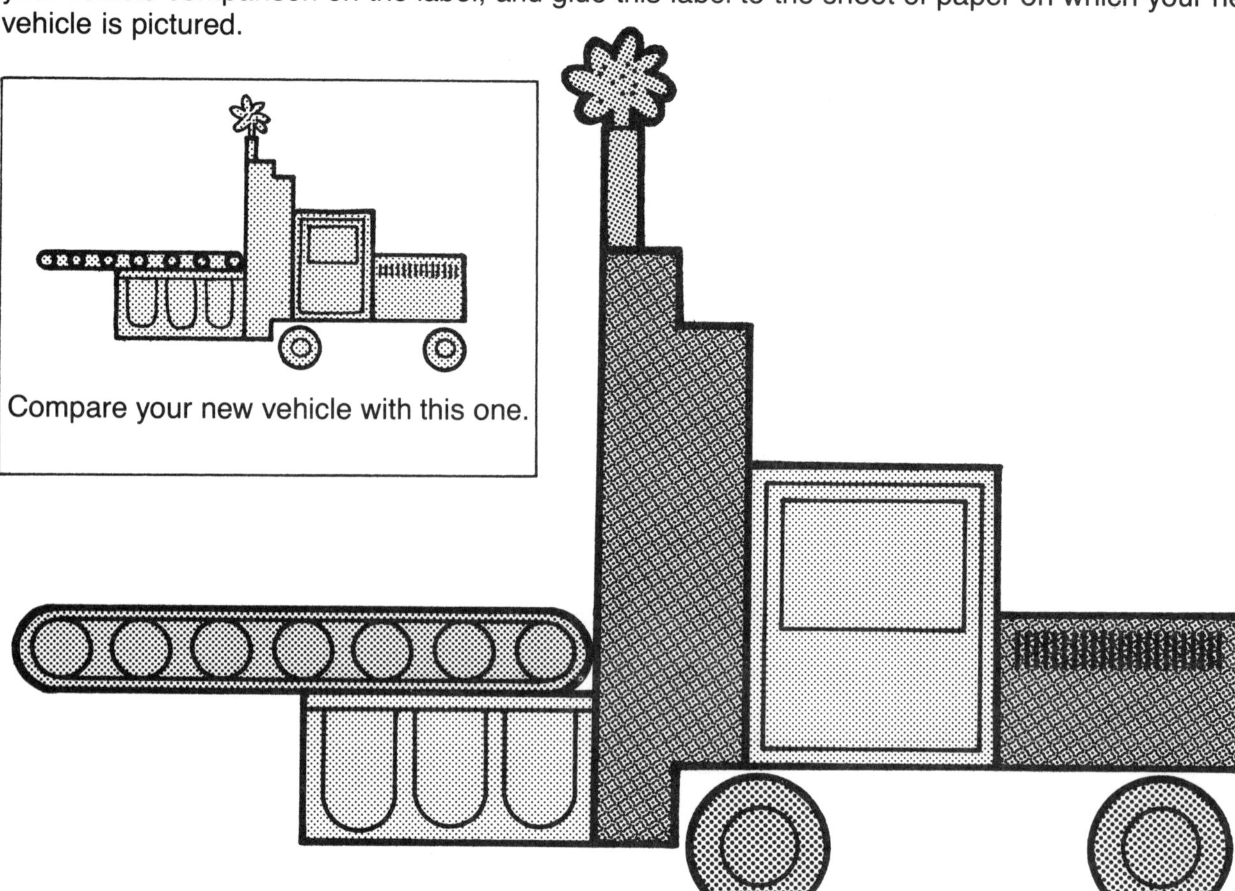

Compare your new vehicle with this one.

My New Vehicle

Name: ______________________

Purpose: ______________________

Results of Vehicle Comparison: ______________________

____

International Inventors
Special Service Award
presented to

____
(your name)

for redesigning the Little Old Woman's shoe
to be of adequate size and to incorporate modern conveniences
so that the woman and all of her children
can live in pleasure and comfort.

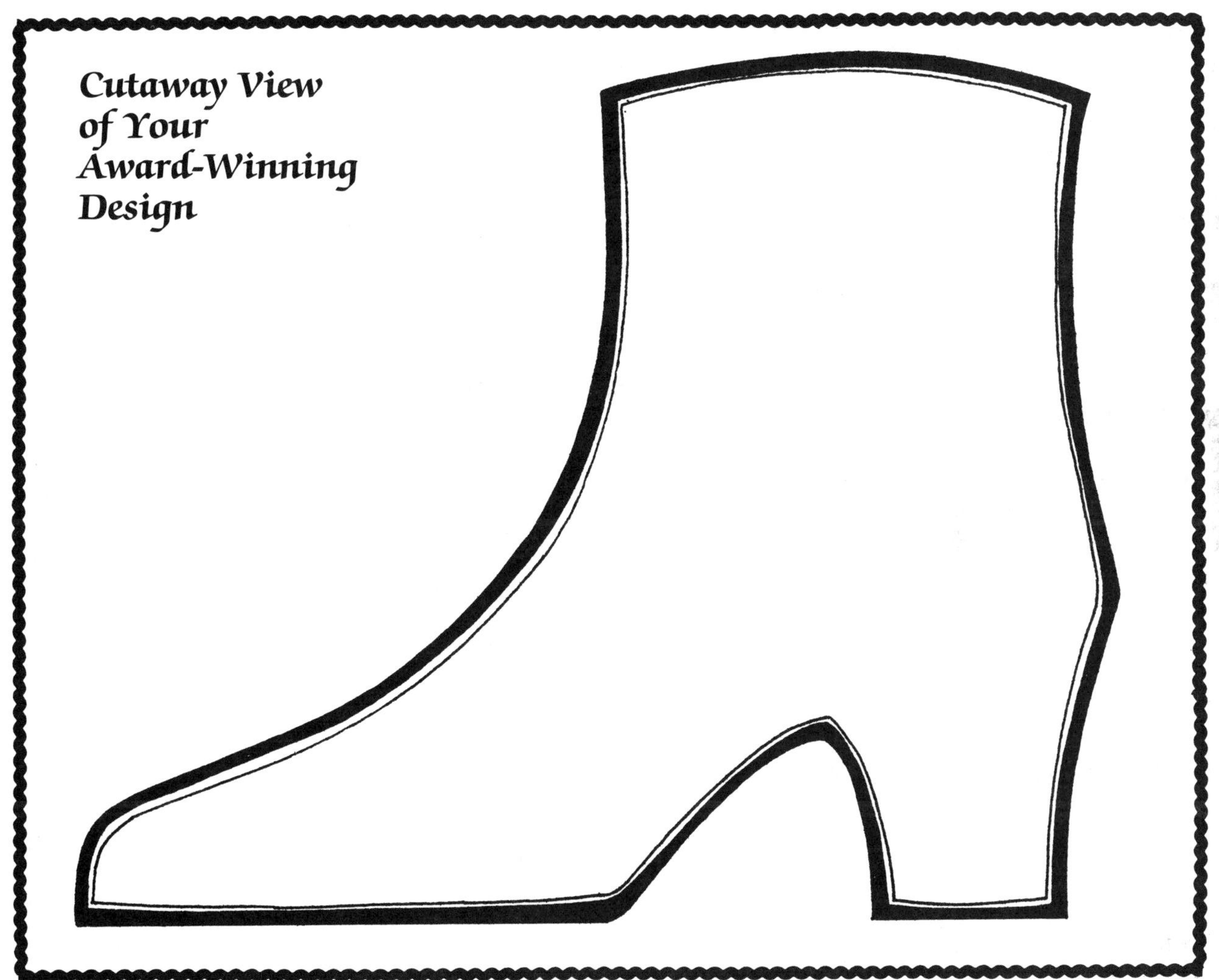

Activity

International Inventors also offers special awards for designing a horn to keep Little Boy Blue awake, a clock that will accommodate Mouse and all of his friends, and a pumpkin shell that has an escape route for Peter Peter Pumpkin Eater's wife. Design one of these objects, and see if you can add another award to your collection.

Name ____________________

Nontechnical Inventions

Not all inventions are scientific or technical. When you create, design, or dream up anything, you are inventing. Try your hand at inventing one or more of the things described below.

Invent a book cover for one of the following titles: *Ages and Ages Ago, Black Hole Adventure, Journey to Freedom, Quest for the Lost Stallion, Revolt of the Robots, The Secret in the Attic.*

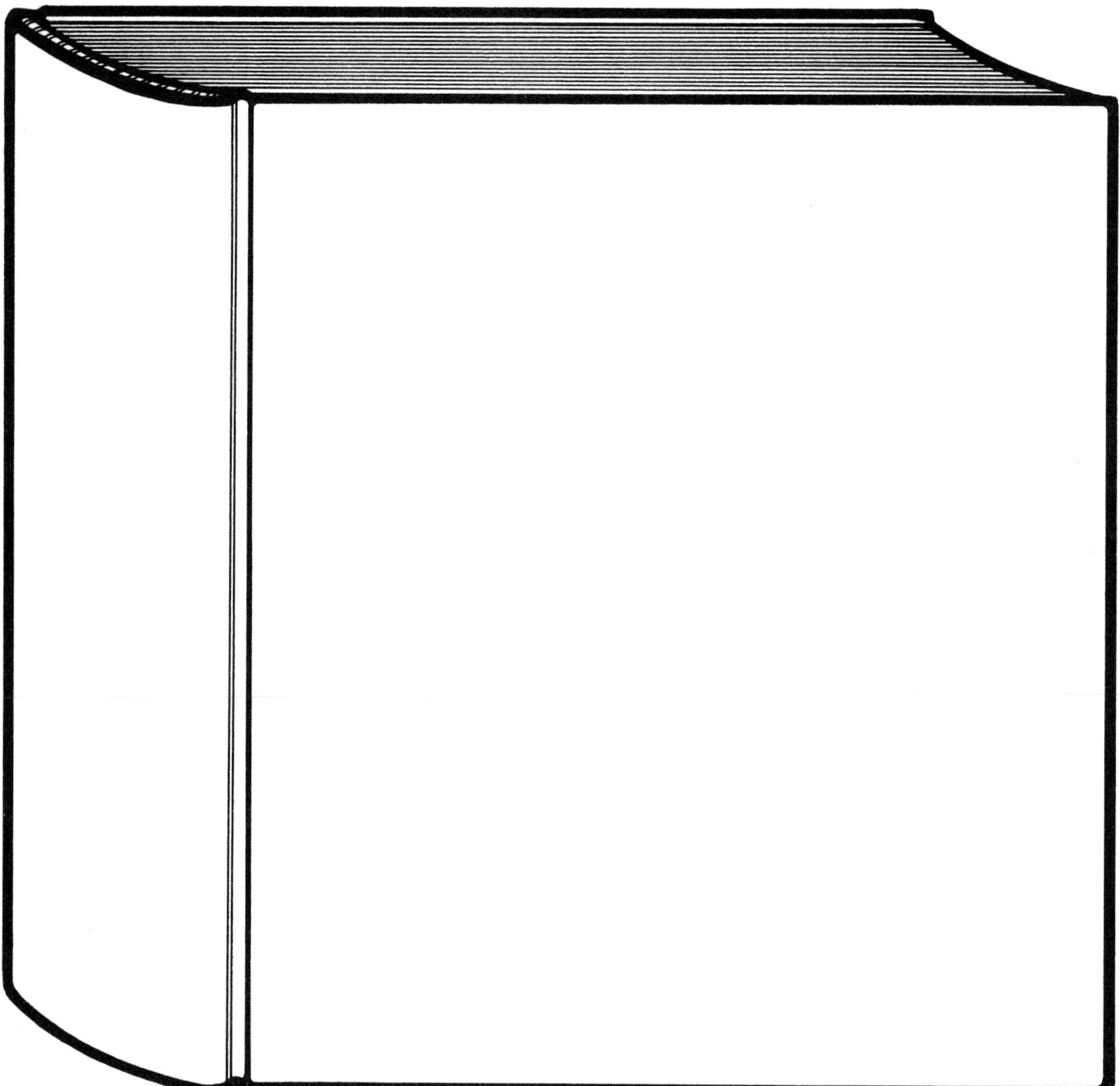

Invent a song that would be enjoyed by young children.

Invent a style of clothing that would be worn by teenagers, now or in the future.

Invent a dessert for someone who loves chocolate, ice cream, and peanut butter.

Invent a new way of learning how to do addition.

Name ______________________________

Leonardo da Vinci

Leonardo da Vinci was born in Tuscany, a region in west-central Italy, in 1452 during the Renaissance, a time in which people all over Europe were taking a fresh look at their world. Leonardo not only exhibited endless patience and boundless curiosity, but also seemed to have a natural grasp of scientific and engineering principles. Because he wanted to understand all that was around him, the world became his laboratory. Everything he did—his artwork, his scientific discoveries, and his mechanical inventions—began with careful observations. Nothing was so small, so ordinary, or so seemingly unimportant that it escaped his notice—not even the buzzing of a bee, the flight of a bird, or the dropping of water into a pool. He labored tirelessly to dispel mysteries and to enlighten the world with discoveries that resulted from both observation and experimentation.

Today, we consider Leonardo to have been a genius in the areas of architecture, biology, engineering, mathematics, meteorology, optics, painting, and sculpture. He invented many ballistic machines, designed the first airplane, was the first to develop the concept of the helicopter, and the first to invent the diving suit. Recently, Italian engineers, working from Leonardo's labeled diagrams and detailed notes and sketches, constructed two hundred working models of his various inventions.

Leonardo studied human anatomy so that he would understand the ways in which the muscles worked and could represent them accurately in his art. He was the first to explain how the heart circulated the blood within the body.

Leonardo da Vinci has only lately been given credit for many of his discoveries and inventions because his notes, which were disorganized and written in mirror writing, have only recently been deciphered and published.

Activities

1. Leonardo da Vinci lived from 1452 until 1519. What important historical events took place during these sixty-seven years? Make a detailed time line for this period.
2. Leonardo da Vinci kept extensive notebooks in which he listed things that puzzled him, wrote about his observations, drew pictures to show how things worked, and described his ideas and inventions. Portions of Leonardo's *Notebooks* have now been published in both standard book and facsimile format. If possible, visit a library and look at pages from Leonardo's *Notebooks*. Then, for two weeks or longer, keep a notebook in which you write questions for which you need answers, list problems you'd like to solve, and describe and illustrate your own observations and inventions.
3. For many years, Leonardo da Vinci was far more famous for his magnificent paintings than for his inventions. He loved outward shapes and forms. He experimented with the subtle flow of light into dark and accurately represented the relationship between outward gestures and expressions and inner feelings and emotions. Many of Leonardo's paintings are reproduced in full color in art books. Go to a library, locate one or more of these books, and study his paintings and sketches. Then, choose your favorite and tell why you like it.
4. Speculate about what Leonardo might be inventing if he were alive today.
5. After you have done some research on Leonardo da Vinci, decide which three of his inventions are the most important. On a separate sheet of paper, briefly describe each one of these inventions, and then explain why you have selected it.

Name ______________________

Construct a Contraption

Cartoonist Rube Goldberg (1883–1970) began drawing fantastic machines more than fifty years ago. His cartoons depicted Boob McNutt, Lala Palooza, and a witty character named Professor Butts, who used one absurdly complex contraption after another to turn the simplest tasks, such as scratching his back or washing his dishes, into incredibly complicated ordeals. Goldberg was making fun of the idea that new methods *always* represent better ways of doing things and that new inventions are *always* improvements. Goldberg's satirical look at problem solving through mechanical contrivance earned him the Pulitzer Prize for editorial cartooning in 1948.

Rude goldfish, **A**, sticks out tongue at cat, **B**, which reacts with indignant hiss. Hiss awakens snake, **C**, which rises from basket and hits head on shelf, **D**, causing egg, **E**, to fall into frying pan, **F**. Eventually, smoke, **G**, from burned egg sets off smoke alarm, **H**. Noise disrupts radar of passing bat, **I**, which crashes into wire, **J**. This lifts and lights match, **K**, setting off cannon, **L**, and sending cannonball down chute, **M**. Cannonball lands on bellows, **N**, which blow out candles on birthday cake, **O**.

Activities

1. Design and draw plans for a contraption using simple machines (levers, pulleys, and wedges). Then build your contraption and display it in a class or school **Contraption Fair**.
2. Use Goldberg concepts to invent a pizza-making machine.

Name ___________________________

Electronic Braces

Many boys and girls have wished that they could substantially reduce the time orthodontic braces had to remain on their teeth. Thanks to a dentist named Zeev Davidovitch, their wish may soon come true.

Previously, the long wearing time has been necessary because teeth-straightening is a three-part process. The teeth must be moved slowly in the jaw, the moved teeth must settle into a new place, and the bone must harden around them to hold them firmly in position.

Davidovitch has invented electronic braces that work in connection with the conventional mechanical braces being worn by a patient and shorten the wearing time considerably. Davidovitch's electronic braces consist of three tiny batteries, a transistor, and a resistor—all contained in a packet no thicker than two nickels placed one atop the other. This packet is hidden under the patient's lip. The electronic current generated by the packet is used to move the teeth into position and to stimulate rapid growth of new bone to hold the teeth in place. Happily, the wearer doesn't feel a thing!

Activities

1. Do some research to discover the inventions that have revolutionized dentistry during the past fifty years. If possible, talk with your dentist about some of these inventions and about how they have affected his or her practice. Present your findings in a chart, mobile, or poster.
2. Write a paragraph or two in which you describe what dentistry will be like in the twenty-first century.
3. Think about a dental problem that you or some member of your family has or about some aspect of dental hygiene that you find particularly irksome. Then invent a device to solve your problem or to make the task less tedious.

Name ____________________

An Artificial Heart

On December 2, 1982, modern medical history was made when the first permanent artificial heart was implanted in the chest of Barney Clark, a dentist from Seattle, Washington. This spectacular achievement culminated twenty-five years of research in which a team of physicians and other scientists experimented with a variety of man-made replacements for human body parts.

The artificial heart, designated Jarvik-7, was an aluminum and polyurethane pump with replaceable parts. It was so successful that it dramatically improved the recipient's blood circulation and blood pressure.

More than one hundred days later, Dr. Clark's other vital organs began to fail. Even though Jarvik-7 had beat perfectly 13 million times and was still pumping vigorously, it could not push enough blood through the patient's blood vessels, which had been weakened by his long bout with cardiovascular disease. On March 23, 1983, Dr. Clark died after participating in one of the most dramatic medical experiments of all time.

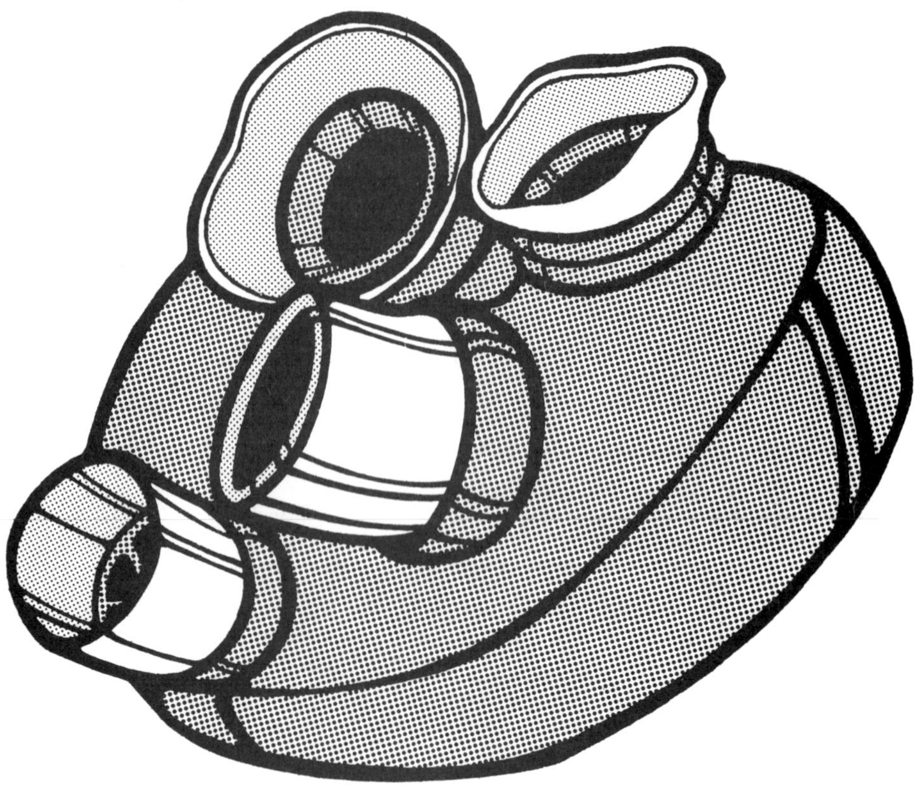

Activities

1. The world's first physician was Imhotep, an Egyptian who lived about 2900 B.C. Choose one of the following historical figures: Avicenna, Galen, Hippocrates, Imhotep, Edward Jenner, Paré, or Vesalius. Do some research to learn about his contributions or importance to the field of medicine. Then present your findings in a written or oral report.
2. The development of new techniques has revolutionized the field of surgery. **Cryosurgery**, for example, is a process in which extreme cold is used to slow the metabolic rate and blood flow and to decrease blood loss during surgery. Speculate about dramatic changes that may take place in surgical procedures within the next twenty years. On a separate sheet of paper, describe and illustrate one of these hypothetical changes.

Name ______________________

A Quick, Safe Exit

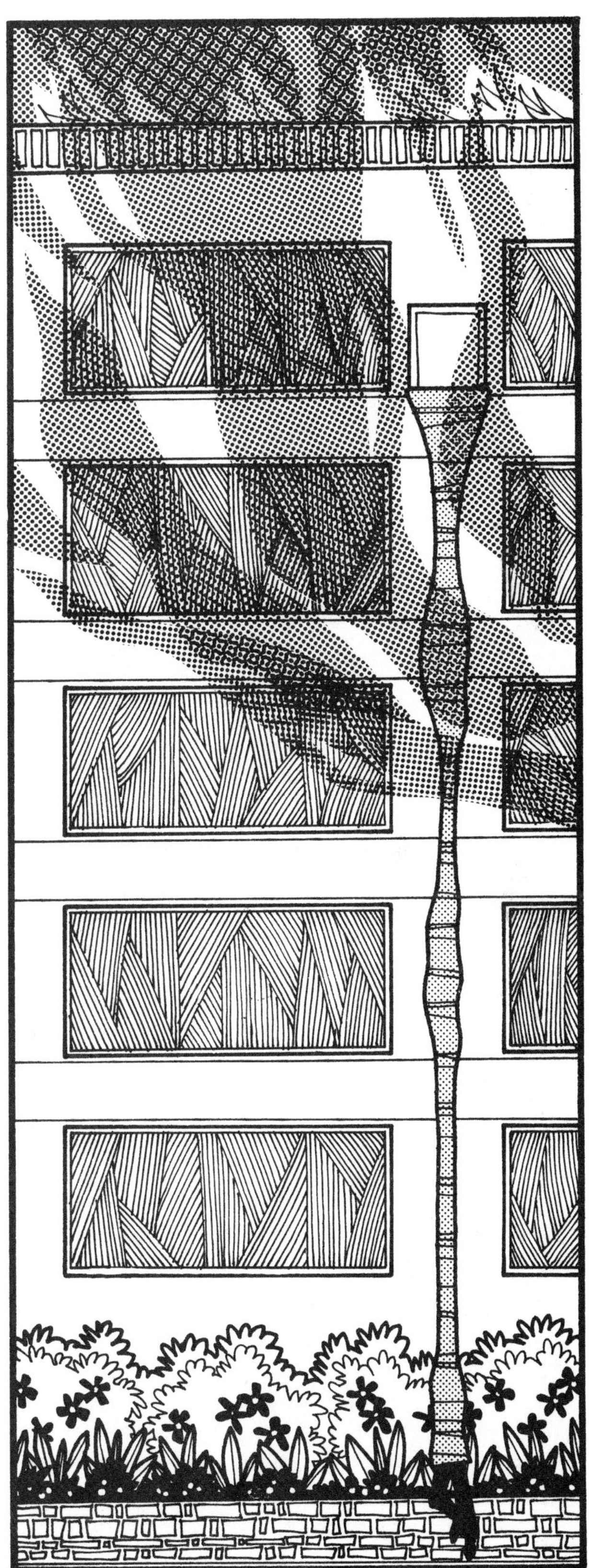

A blaze breaks out in an office building and spreads rapidly. Smoke fills the corridors. People working inside the building sense the danger, leave their desks, and move quickly toward the exits; but they are forced back by dense smoke and extreme heat. These people are apparently trapped in a burning building. What can they do?

In the past, many of them would probably have panicked, jumped from windows, and been seriously injured or killed. The people in this particular office building are luckier than most, however. Their building is equipped with a new fire-escape device invented by a Japanese firm. They are able to make a quick, safe exit by slipping feet first into a vertical chute that is made of a strong, stretchy fiber and is attached to the outside of the building. As each person moves through the chute, it hugs his body to slow his rate of descent so he can land safely.

People who own apartment buildings, factories, hospitals, hotels, and office buildings are considering purchasing these chutes.

Activities

1. Make a list of inventions that are used to protect us or to guide us to safety in an emergency. For example, your list might include fire alarms, fire escapes, fire extinguishers, seat belts, smoke alarms, and so on.
2. Find out about some of the codes and regulations that make public buildings in your hometown safer than they were thirty years ago. Share your findings with the class by means of an oral or a written report.
3. Submarines are very vulnerable. If something goes wrong with their pumps or hydraulic systems while they are underwater, they may be unable to surface. The people inside may be trapped deep in an ocean or lake. Invent a device that would enable sailors to escape from a submarine that could not surface. Take into account the problems created by increased water pressure at great depths.

Name ______________________

Using the Oceans

More than two-thirds of our planet is covered by oceans. These oceans are rich in diamonds, fish, gas, oil, plant life, and many other natural resources. Scientists are exploring the possibilities of using these oceans for living space, for recreation, and as sources of food.

Off the coast of California, scientists are practicing aquaculture—raising giant kelp on rope rafts. The kelp is harvested and converted to methane gas, which is used to supplement the dwindling supply of natural gas.

Some scientists are experimenting with deep-diving research craft, rescue submarines, electronic fish-herding equipment, and even artificial cities beneath the waves. These cities are envisioned as complete living and working environments that would include homes, factories, hospitals, hotels, office buildings, schools, stores, and theaters.

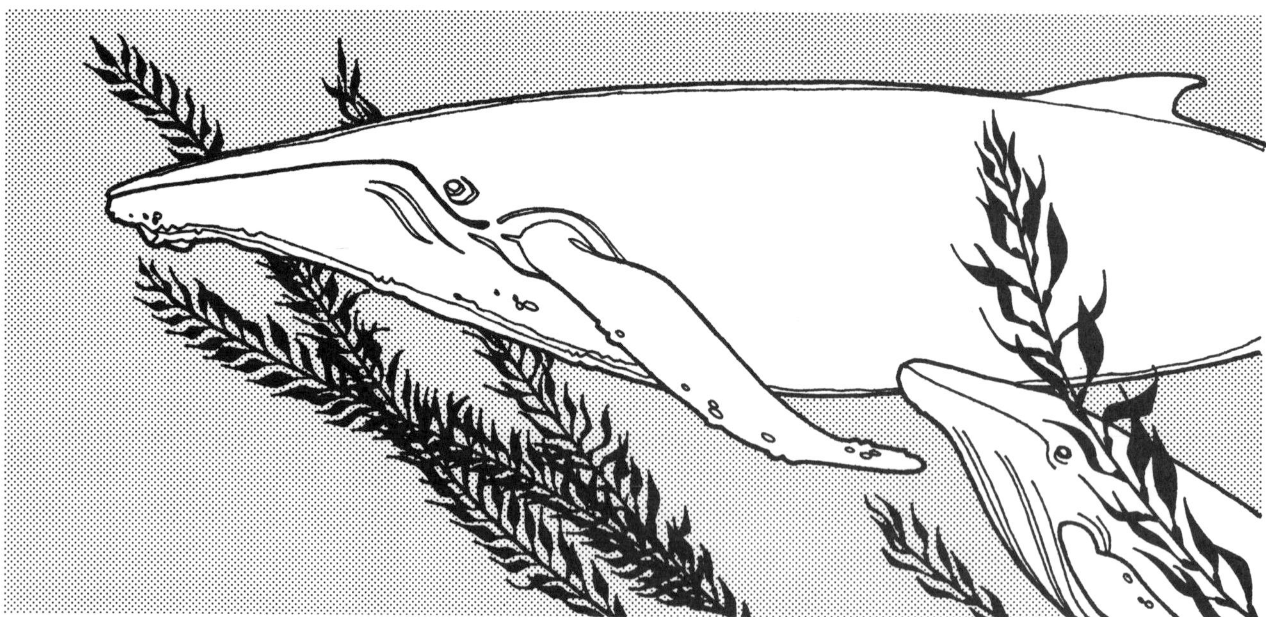

Activities

1. As a scientist-colonizer of the continental shelf, you have been commissioned to invent a device that will make living in this underwater environment easier and more successful and that can be used for work, play, or experimental purposes. On a separate sheet of paper, describe and illustrate your invention. Then explain its application, purpose, or use.

2. As a resident of spaceship earth, you are responsible for protecting the entire biosphere. Many inventions and technological advances threaten to upset the ecosystems in which they are used. For example, the signals from electronic fish-herding equipment interfere with the sonar signals used by dolphins, porpoises, and whales for navigation in the ocean depths. Also, in harvesting food from the ocean, scientists are competing for nourishment with the animals that inhabit this ecosystem.

   First, read about some of the ways in which human technology disturbs the ecological balance of the oceans. Second, list and picture these disturbances and the results of them in a diagram or on a chart. Third, analyze the needs scientists are trying to meet by disturbing the oceans in these ways. Fourth, suggest or invent something that will meet these needs in a less disturbing or destructive way. Fifth, select a single animal or organism within the marine ecosystem, do some research, and then explain its place and value within the system.

Name ______________________________

What Is a Quagga?

Before 1800, vast herds of a unique animal grazed on the grasslands of southern Africa. This animal, called a **quagga**, was of a brownish color and similar in size and shape to a zebra. It was striped from its face to the middle of its body.

Quaggas grazed with other animals, especially ostriches and white-tailed gnus. By grazing together, these three animals were able to protect one another. The ostriches, with their keen vision, could see great distances. The gnus had a highly developed sense of hearing; and, most likely, the quaggas could smell danger while it was still far away.

This partnership worked very well until European settlers arrived in the area and killed thousands of quaggas for food and for their handsome hides, which they shipped back to Europe. The last of the wild quaggas was shot during the 1870s, and the last known quagga died in 1883 in captivity at the Amsterdam zoo.

Activities

1. Speculate as to how the elimination of the quagga might have affected other animals that inhabited the same area, especially the gnus and the ostriches. Then find out about these animals today. Were any of your speculations correct?
2. You will never have the opportunity to see a quagga; but if you could take a step back in time, could you invent something that would protect this unique animal from extinction? For example, you might redesign the quagga so that it would be better able to protect itself, or you might invent an animal preserve that would keep it safe from predators. Use your imagination.
3. The extinction of certain species of animals is a major problem in our world today. Do you think that *all* species should be protected? Why or why not?
4. Many of the species living today are threatened with extinction and need special protection to survive. Find out the names of some of these species. Then think of one or more inventions that might help them in their struggle to survive.

Name ______________________

The Black Hole Express

There may be a million black holes in our galaxy. **Black holes** are the remains of stars. They are so compact that not even light can escape from them.

Some astronomers believe that black holes are the passages through which spaceships of the future will make instantaneous journeys to other parts of the galaxy or universe. These astronomers explain that a spaceship will enter into a funnel of whirling space at just the right angle and velocity, travel to the center of the black hole, and then emerge in another region of space, perhaps several lightyears away.

Pure science fiction? Yes, say some scientists, but others claim that the black hole express will be one means of transportation used in the future much as the pony express was one means of transportation used in the past.

Activities

1. Write a diary, story, or ship's log in which you describe in detail your journey through a black hole to another part of the universe. Include the adventures you have and the discoveries you make while you are there. Illustrate the most exciting parts of your journey.
2. Invent a spacecraft that can withstand the rigors of traveling through a black hole. Draw and label a detailed diagram of your invention.
3. While astronomers dream of travel through space, many scientists are still trying to solve the problems of travel on earth. Among these problems are congestion, inconvenience, pollution, and safety hazards. Invent a transportation device or system for your community which will solve or eliminate at least some of these problems.

Name ____________________

Two Inventions That Changed a Sport

Jumping high has always has been a challenge to athletes, and pole vaulting carries jumpers the highest. In the 1896 Olympics, William Hoyt of the United States vaulted 10 feet 9 3/4 inches. Fifty-six years later, U.S. athlete Bob Richards soared over the bar at 14 feet 11 1/8 inches, nearly five feet higher. This difference was made possible in part by a change in pole design. Early vaulters had used bamboo or wooden poles; later vaulters used poles that were made of steel or a metal alloy.

No vaulter jumped higher than 16 feet until 1964. In that year, Olympic vaulters switched from metal to fiberglass poles. Because fiberglass poles bend on takeoff, they give jumpers greater lift and allow them to make much higher leaps. Using the new pole, U.S. athlete Fred Hansen won a gold medal in Tokyo, Japan with a jump of 16 feet 8 3/4 inches.

By the end of 1964, the record height for pole vaulting was 17 feet. The winner of the 1972 Olympics in Munich, Germany, cleared 18 feet 1/2 inch. At the 1988 Olympics in Seoul, Korea, Sergei Bubka of the U.S.S.R. won a gold medal with a jump of 19 feet 9 1/4 inches.

While new pole designs have changed pole vaulting, many coaches feel that some of the credit for improved athletic performance in this and other sports should go to better nutrition and improved training techniques.

Activities

1. Look up and list the heights reached by the pole vaulters who have won gold medals in Olympic competition. Then represent these heights by year on a line or bar graph. What trends do you notice? What conclusions can you draw?
2. Invent a new piece of equipment to improve one of the following sports: baseball, basketball, football, ice skating, soccer, swimming, or tennis. Consider comfort, performance, and/or safety. Draw and label a diagram of your invention. Then write a paragraph in which you explain its application, purpose, or use.
3. People often compare the performances of athletes today with those of athletes fifty and more years ago. Is it fair to compare performances when the equipment used has changed radically? Debate this issue with a friend.
4. To what degree does the equipment used in sporting events affect the results, or outcomes, of these events? Debate this question with a friend.

Name ______________________

Adventure in Inner Space

Imagine yourself being reduced to microscopic size, climbing aboard a mini atomic submarine, and being injected into an artery of a sick man to search out the disease that is plaguing him and destroy it with rays from a laser gun. Isaac Asimov used just such a premise as the basis for his novel, *Fantastic Voyage*, published during the 1960s.

Now you have the opportunity to take a fact-finding fantasy journey to mysterious places within your own body. Your mission is to explore and report on some particular organ or structure. You must be careful of the dangers involved in inner-body travel: the possibility of being mistaken for an intruder by infection-fighting white blood cells, the high-frequency sounds near the eardrum, and the rapids as you approach the heart.

To prepare for your journey, close your eyes, relax your muscles, and use your imagination to invent a mini-machine that will allow you to travel inside your own body. Once you have imagined the vehicle, imagine yourself inside it and go!

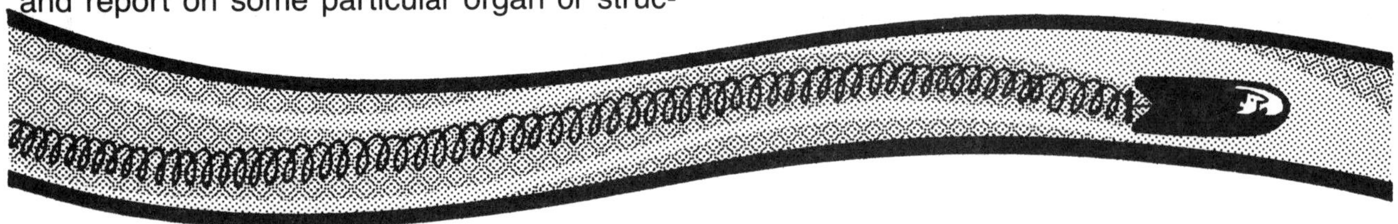

Official Report of An Inner Space Explorer

Describe your travel vehicle and attach an illustration.

____

____

____

List the itinerary for your journey. Name the points of interest that you will visit in the order in which you plan to visit them.

____

____

____

____

____

____

On a separate sheet of paper, write and illustrate an account of your most interesting or exciting adventure.

Name ________________

Sack-a-Snack

Invent a vending machine children can use to make their own nutritious snacks. On a separate sheet of paper, draw a picture of your machine. Give it a name, and label the snack choices that are available. For example, you might include nuts and seeds, dried fruits, grains, and vegetable chips among the food choices. Write simple instructions so that other people will know how to use your machine.

Use your vending machine to create a custom-mixed snack. Write the proportions for it on the recipe card below. Then give your snack a name.

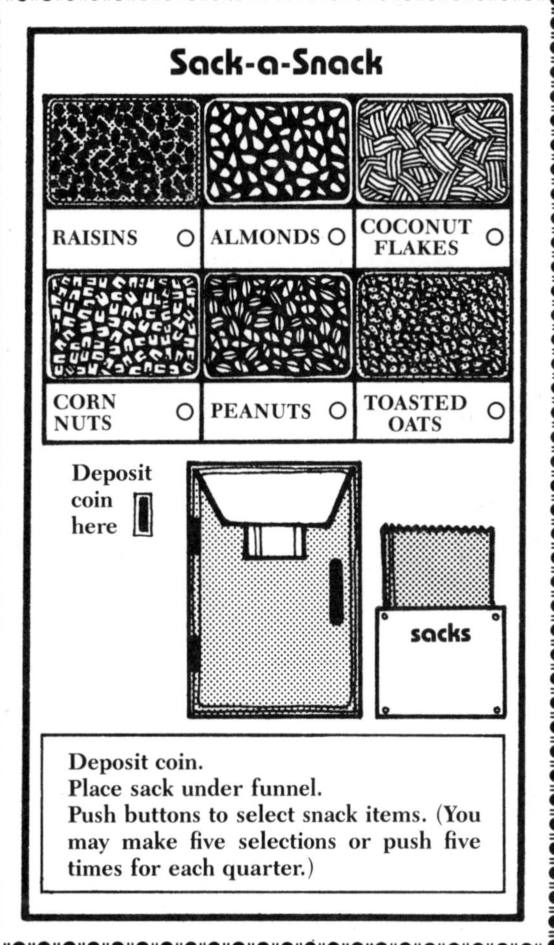

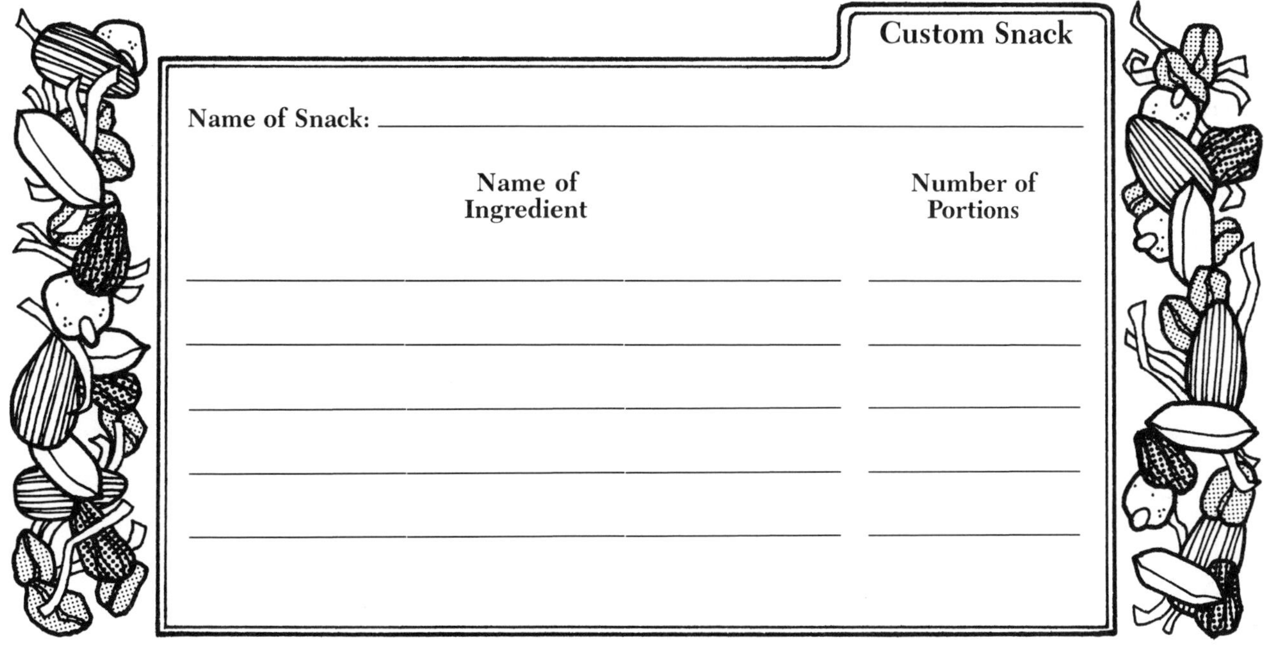

Name ____________________

Choosing to Chew

Chewing gum is popular the world over. It is readily available in drug and grocery stores. Today, people chew gum for pleasure; but many years ago, they had other reasons for choosing to chew.

Hundreds of years ago, prehistoric people chewed the sticky resins from various trees. American Indians chewed spruce resin as a thirst quencher, and early settlers copied this practice.

More than one thousand years ago, the Maya, Indians of southern Mexico, chewed **chicle**, a pinkish to reddish-brown substance they refined from the sap of the sapodilla tree. To get this sap, they cut zigzag gashes in the bark of the trees and collected it in bags, which they tied to the tree trunks.

Chicle, which is still the basis for chewing gums made today, was probably first introduced into the United States by the Mexican general Santa Anna, who seized the Alamo in 1836 in an attempt to crush the Texas Revolution.

A process for making chewing gum from chicle was patented in 1869 by William and Semple. In 1891, William Wrigley, Jr., an American industrialist, founded a company in Chicago, Illinois, for the purpose of manufacturing chewing gum. His company experimented with different textures and added peppermint and spearmint flavorings.

In the Wrigley factory, blocks of chicle imported from Mexico and Central America were ground, melted, cleared of impurities in a whirling vat, and then sterilized. Sugar, corn syrup, and mint flavorings were added to the liquid. As it cooled and hardened, the gum was rolled through machinery that pressed it into sheets. Then it was cut into sticks, wrapped, and packaged for sale.

During the early twentieth century, chewing gum became very popular throughout the United States; and it was not long before this country was the major producer, exporter, and consumer of it. Today, though much has changed in the gum industry, peppermint and spearmint are still among the most popular chewing gum flavors; but flavor variations include cherry, cinnamon, licorice, strawberry, and watermelon.

Activities

1. Do some research to learn more about the steps followed to make gum. Represent these steps on a labeled diagram or chart.
2. Do some research to learn more about William Wrigley, Jr., and the company he founded. Is it still in operation today?
3. Talk to your dentist about the relationship between chewing gum and the decay process. Does he or she favor the use of sugarless gum? Why or why not? Represent the decay process in a series of sketches or diagrams. Then represent the relationship between gum chewing and tooth decay on a line or bar graph.
4. Dream up a new bubble gum that produces *very unusual* bubbles. Draw a picture of one of the bubbles.
5. Name your gum, and design a wrapper for it.
6. Create a short radio or television commercial to sell your gum.
7. Design a trading card to be included in the gum package.

Name ______________________

An Effervescent Invention

Soda pop is a drink usually made by adding flavoring and sweet syrup to soda water. **Soda water**, in turn, is a solution of carbon dioxide in water. It is called "soda water" because baking soda (sodium bicarbonate) was originally used to prepare it.

Carbon dioxide is a colorless, almost odorless, gaseous compound of carbon and oxygen. It can be dissolved in water; and the resulting solution, which has weak acid properties, is known as **carbonic acid**. When carbon dioxide is dissolved in water under pressure, it produces the effervescence we observe in soda pop as bubbles and foam.

Crystal Cola, Apple Crunch, Strawberry Fizz—which new soda pop would you buy? Inventing and successfully marketing a new soft drink is a very complicated process that involves far more than just choosing an interesting flavor. The color must be carefully selected, the container must be designed, and an advertising campaign must be skillfully planned.

Activities

1. Complete this chart for the three soda pops mentioned above. Then dream up and include a soda pop of your own.

Name	Color	Flavor	Container Design
Crystal Cola		*just a hint of peppermint*	
Apple Crunch	*light green*		
Strawberry Fizz			

2. Do some research to learn about the steps in the chemical process by which carbonic acid produces effervescence. Represent these steps in a labeled diagram or chart.
3. Compare the process by which people produce soda pop with the process by which nature produces sparkling mineral water. In what ways are these two processes the same? In what ways are they different?
4. Conduct a survey to discover which soda pop students in your class like best. Analyze the results of your survey, and present them in the form of a chart, graph, or table.
5. Conduct a test to determine the extent to which taste influences soda pop selection. Blindfold students so that they cannot see the color or the container. Have them taste the soda pops rated most highly in the survey and indicate their preferences. Analyze and evaluate your results. What factors might account for any significant differences between the survey results and the taste test results?

Name ______________________

Architectural Inventing

Architects spend hours dreaming about and experimenting with building designs that are both functional and pleasing to the eye, and that make use of new building materials and techniques.

You have been given an opportunity to "reinvent" your bedroom. Will you put your room underground or use flexible or movable materials? Will you make your room a different shape? How will you change the furniture? What will you invent to make your room more comfortable, more interesting, and/or more entertaining?

Consider these questions and then redesign your bedroom in the space below.

Name ______________________

Invent a Game

Card and board games were as popular thousands of years ago as they are today. **Senet** was one of the most popular board games in ancient Egypt. It was played by peasants in the sand using stones for playing pieces and by pharaohs on magnificent boards with pieces made of earthenware, ivory, and rare woods. **Chess**, another popular board game, originated in Asia and spread westward around A.D. 500. Yet another board game, **Backgammon**, is also very old. The Roman emperor Nero, who lived from A.D. 37 to A.D. 68, is reported to have gambled vast sums of money while playing an ancient version of Backgammon.

Inventors today work to devise highly motivating and creative games. Some of these games are based on fantasy, science fiction, and sports themes. Others are complicated strategy games, educational games, and even new versions of old favorites.

Activities

1. Invent your own game. Choose a subject or theme for your game, and give it a name. Decide on a purpose for your game, and write rules and instructions for it. Make a game board and whatever question and chance cards are needed. Include an answer booklet, dice, a spinner, playing pieces, and/or tokens, if necessary.
2. Play the game with your friends.
3. Analyze your experience playing the game and then make whatever changes are necessary in the equipment or the rules to make the game more challenging, more effective, or more fun.
4. Conduct a survey of the members of your class or your family to discover what types of games they like best. Analyze the results of your survey and present them in the form of a table, chart, or graph.
5. Based on the results of your survey, write a composite description of the "ideal" game. Then invent a game to match this description.
6. Select several commercially designed games, play them, and compare them on the basis of interest, involvement, and innovation. Which one do you prefer? Why?

Name ____________________

Inventors

Life is becoming increasingly complex and more rapid. For example, there are eight thousand products on supermarket shelves today, compared with only three thousand products not long ago; and nearly half of today's products will be obsolete in five years! Where do all of these products come from? Many of them are inventions. They are the work of inventors and innovators.

Why do people invent? People invent for a variety of reasons. They are curious about that which is new, untried, or unknown. They are stimulated by a natural desire to question and to learn. Because of past inventions, they have a certain amount of leisure time in which to dream and to experiment with new ideas. They want to solve a problem, to improve a product, to achieve fame, or to help humanity.

While inventors share some of the same characteristics and reasons for inventing, they are *not* all alike or of one type. Some inventors are old, some are young. Some inventors are wealthy, while others are poor; some have received years of formal schooling, while others are largely self-taught. Some inventors are men, while others are women.

Many women inventors are relatively unknown. For example, few people realize that Eli Whitney based his cotton gin prototype on a design by Catherine L. Green, his landlady. The H.J. Heinz Company originated when Mrs. Heinz began selling her homemade pickles. These women and many other female inventors were not given credit for their inventions because, under nineteenth-century law, they did not have the right to own property and, therefore, could not file for patents to protect their inventions or go into business to manufacture and market them.

Activity

The names of inventors are often closely associated with their inventions or with something that is related to their inventions. Read this list of inventors, and see how many of their inventions you can identify. On a separate sheet of paper, list the names. Beside each name, identify or describe the invention with which you think that name is associated. Then check yourself by looking up the names of these inventors or their inventions in an encyclopedia.

Benz
Birdseye
Bissell
Braille
Colt
Daguerre
Daimler
Diesel
Dunlop
Eastman
Evinrude
Fahrenheit
Gillette
Goodyear
Land
Otis
Pasteur
Pullman
Roentgen
Sikorsky
Volta
Yale

Name ______________________

The Cone Connection

Frozen desserts have been enjoyed for hundreds of years in many parts of the world, but they have not always been as easy to make as they are today. The Aztecs, an Indian people who dominated central Mexico during the fifteenth century, lived in an area that was sometimes hot and usually dry. Although they were accomplished engineers and built beautiful buildings, they had no reliable means of refrigeration. They could heat some foods over a fire and cool other foods in the waters of a lake or stream, but they could not make any food cold enough to freeze. What they could do, however, was send runners into the mountains to bring back snow, which they ate as a refreshing delicacy on hot, dry days.

Ice cream as we know it probably originated in Italy during the seventeenth century as a flavored water ice. It quickly spread to France and England and, from there, to America early in the eighteenth century.

Real ice cream is a frozen food made from milk fat and solids, sugar, and flavoring. In addition, it may contain coloring, a stabilizer (usually gelatin), eggs, and bits of candy, fruit, or nuts. Ice cream was first manufactured on a commercial scale in Baltimore, Maryland, in 1851. Since that time, ice-cream-making has become an important industry in the United States, and ice-cream-eating has become a refreshing pastime.

According to one source, the ice cream cone was born on a hot day when a sidewalk vendor ran out of dishes in which to serve his frozen confection. Being an innovative soul, he bought a waffle from the cart next to his, rolled it into a cone shape, and set a scoop of ice cream atop the wider end.

Activities

1. From Tenochtitlán, their capital city, the Aztecs administered an empire that lasted less than two hundred years but extended throughout Mesoamerica. Find out more about the Aztecs and their culture. Share what you learn in a written or oral report.
2. Taste some real Italian ices. Compare them with ice cream. In what ways are these two frozen desserts similar? In what ways are they different? Which one do you like best? Why?
3. Follow a recipe to make homemade ice cream. Then enjoy it in a dish or on a cone.
4. There have been relatively few lasting variations in the ice cream cone since its invention. Cones have been made with and without sugar. They have been made with pointed and with flattened bottoms. There was an attempt at one time to make the cone top square so that it would hold a prewrapped ice cream cube; but while this shape was popular with ice cream servers, it never really caught on among ice cream eaters. Invent a cone to revolutionize the ice cream industry. Consider flavoring the cone, changing its shape or texture, varying its size, or making it dripless. On a separate sheet of paper, draw and label a picture of your cone or write a paragraph in which you describe it in detail.

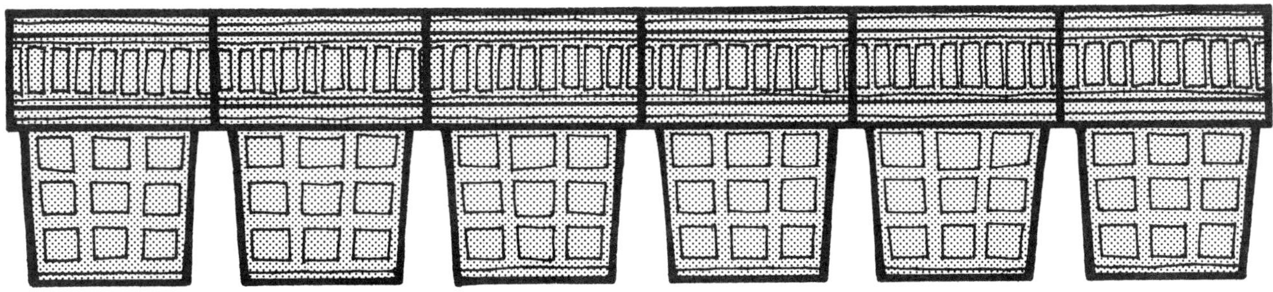

Name ____________________

Intriguing Inventions

The strange objects pictured below are actually patented inventions. Can you figure out what each one was designed to do? Look at each picture carefully, and then circle the appropriate letter.

1. a. double head wrench
   b. piano tuner
   c. duck call
   d. dental floss holder

2. a. aquarium cleaner
   b. paint sprayer
   c. hearing aid
   d. snake case

3. a. gopher trap
   b. toe clip
   c. pig muzzle
   d. soap holder

4. a. potato spade
   b. gutter scraper
   c. log splitter
   d. hay knife

5. a. melon slicer
   b. carpet stretcher
   c. letter opener
   d. ice cutter

6. a. handcuff
   b. spaghetti tongs
   c. cattle leader
   d. bike lock

7. a. nutmeg grater
   b. fish scaler
   c. fly trap
   d. paint strainer

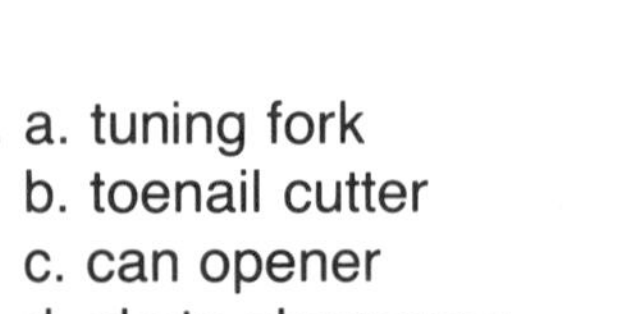

8. a. tuning fork
   b. toenail cutter
   c. can opener
   d. skate sharpener

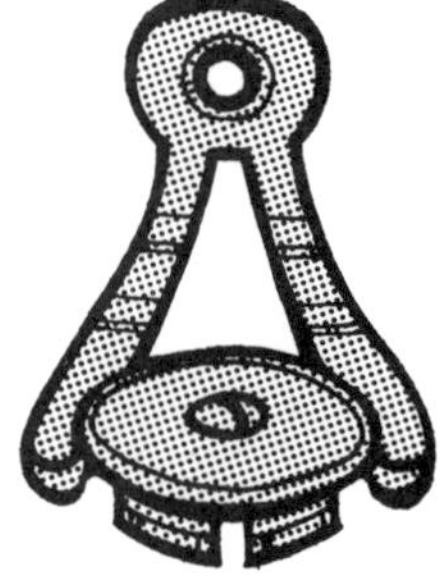

Name ______________________

Protect Your Ideas

To protect your inventions, you must obtain patents. Patents are issued by the United States Patent and Trademark Office. During its 187 years of operation, this office has issued patents for more than four million inventions. Patents are issued for new, useful, original, or improved machines, methods, processes, products, or substances. They give inventors the right to exclude all other persons and companies from making, using, or selling their inventions. To apply for a patent, submit a description of your invention and a statement telling what makes it new and useful to

Commissioner of Patents and Trademarks
Patent and Trademark Office
Washington, D.C. 20231

Activities

1. Some countries do not honor the patent laws of the United States. First think about the problems that their failure to do so might cause, and then make a list of several possible solutions to these problems.
2. While inventions are protected by patents, original written works are protected by copyrights. First, do some research to learn more about patents and copyrights. Then, prepare a simple chart or table on which you compare these two forms of idea protection.

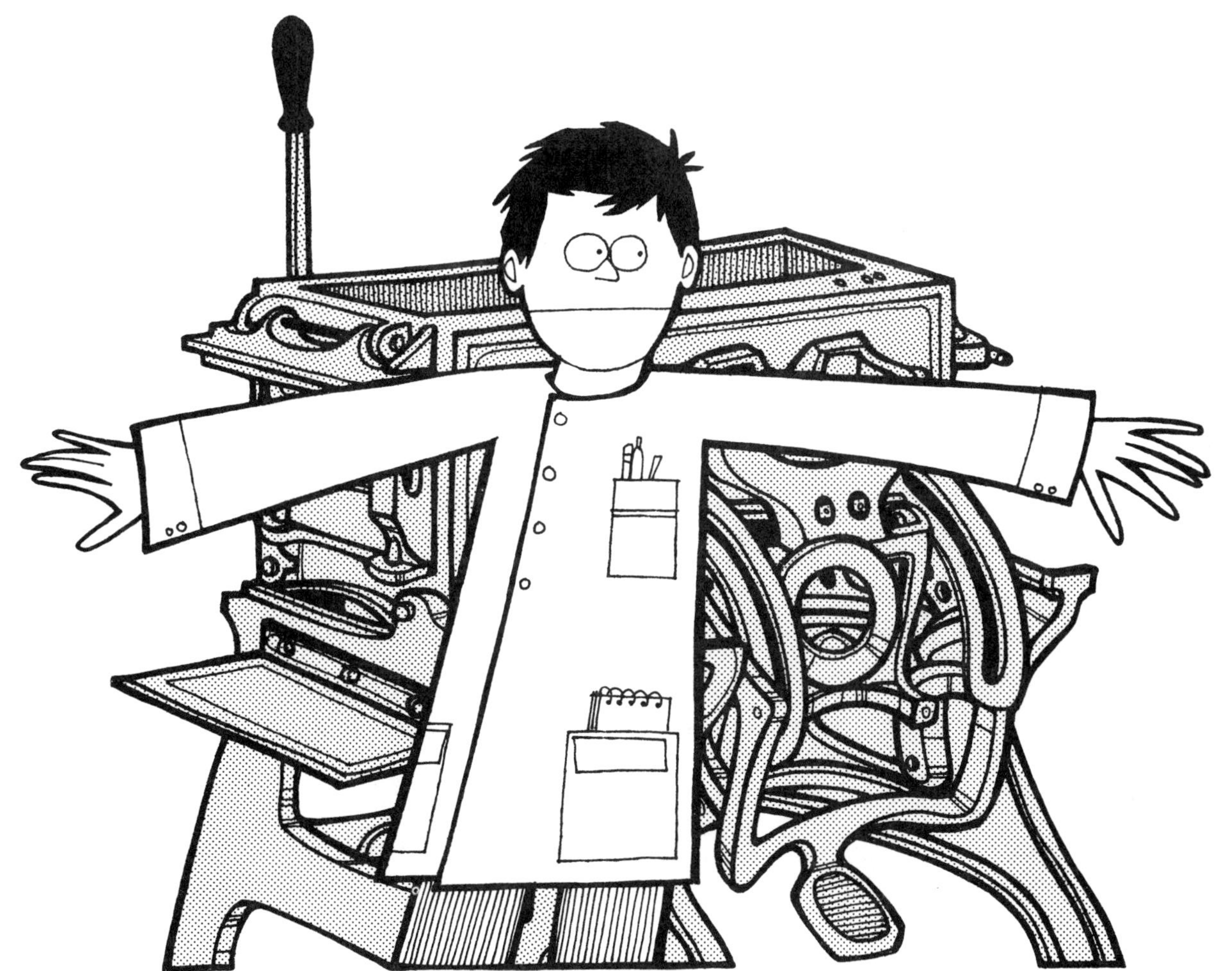

Correlated Activities

Architecture

Invent the perfect pet house, bedroom, playroom, video room, or tree house. Draw and label a picture of your invention.

Language Arts

Team up with several of your friends to write and publish a school or neighborhood newspaper. Include interviews with interesting people, lost-and-found or advice columns, stories about important sports events, and other newsy items.

Imagine that you have been hired by the president of KTOY-TV and given a budget of one million dollars to create a hit television show. Write a brief description of your show, and include a few sample pages from the script.

Create a unique logo for your class to depict the special interests and abilities of some of its members.

Imagine that you can travel back in time to personally interview Alexander Graham Bell, George Washington Carver, Thomas Alva Edison, Benjamin Franklin, Leonardo da Vinci, or some other inventor of your choice. Write a news report or a feature story based on your imaginary experience.

Physical Education

You are the camp counselor for fifteen boys and girls. Today you are in charge of sports activities; however, your supplies have not arrived, and the only things you can find are a rope, a baseball, and a cardboard box. Using only these three pieces of equipment, quickly invent a game that will keep this group of children involved for one full hour. Describe your game, and write out the rules for it on a separate sheet of paper.

Invent a miniature golf course that could be used easily by players in wheelchairs. What problems must you solve? What design elements must you include?

Invent a game that might be considered by the Olympic Committee for inclusion in the Summer or Winter Olympics. Explain why your game is unique, why athletes would enjoy playing it, and why spectators would enjoy watching it.

Correlated Activities
(continued)

Science

If you have ever spent much time cooking, you know that food preparation often takes time and can be a complicated process. Think of an invention that would save time and/or simplify a common kitchen task. Draw and label a diagram of your invention.

Your city is faced with a serious housing shortage. The only available lot for building is the lot used by neighborhood boys and girls for their after-school sports activities. Invent a complex that will supply the necessary housing and preserve some of the open areas without harming the environment.

Invent a snack or dessert that is both nutritious and delicious. Write the recipe for it on a separate sheet of paper. With your teacher's or parent's permission, follow your recipe to make your invention, and share some of it with classmates or friends.

Have you ever dreamed of owning a perfect pet? What qualities would your perfect pet possess? Invent this pet. Think about the qualities and characteristics of unusual animals like anteaters, armadillos, and boa constrictors. Remember to consider your own physical and emotional needs and those of your pet. On a separate sheet of paper, draw a picture of your pet and explain why it is perfect. Create an advertisement for this pet.

Social Studies

A pharaoh has hired you to build a tamperproof pyramid so that all of his precious gems and golden statues will be permanently safe from grave robbers and curious archaeologists. On a large sheet of paper, draw a cross-section of the pyramid. Include and label each device you have dreamed up to make it tamperproof.

Name ______________________

Posttest

Complete each of the sentences below by circling the correct letter.

1. Inventors have special qualities that enable them to create. Among these qualities is
   a. magic.
   b. curiosity.
   c. luck.
   d. strength.
2. One reason an inventor decides to invent is to
   a. solve a problem.
   b. publish a book.
   c. fulfill a contract.
   d. file for a patent.
3. A famous inventor who lived during the Renaissance was named
   a. Leonardo da Vinci.
   b. Thomas Alva Edison.
   c. Alexander Graham Bell.
   d. Edward Jenner.
4. The inventor who first developed the concept of the helicopter was
   a. Zeev Davidovitch.
   b. Igor Ivan Sikorsky.
   c. Rube Goldberg.
   d. Leonardo da Vinci.
5. Rube Goldberg created cartoons to poke fun at
   a. professors.
   b. old discoveries.
   c. new inventions.
   d. scientists.
6. Barney Clark was
   a. the recipient of the first artificial heart.
   b. a builder of underwater cities.
   c. the inventor of electronic braces.
   d. a designer of fire escape chutes.
7. A new method for straightening teeth makes use of
   a. thoracic surgery.
   b. biofeedback.
   c. electric current.
   d. stronger wires.

Complete sentences 8 and 9 by circling the letter of the one *incorrect* answer.

8. Based on oceanographic experiments, scientists have already devised methods for
   a. growing kelp.
   b. herding fish.
   c. establishing underwater cities.
   d. harnessing ocean currents.
9. The U.S Patent Office will issue a patent for
   a. a new machine.
   b. an improved process.
   c. a useful product.
   d. a new form of electricity.

10. Two of the following four items are discoveries, and two are inventions. Write **D** on the line in front of each discovery. Write **I** on the line in front of each invention.
    _____ a. uranium
    _____ b. safety matches
    _____ c. plow
    _____ d. electricity

Answer Key

Page 8, Pretest

1. a
2. a
3. b
4. b
5. c
6. d
7. a
8. c
9. c
10. b

Page 9, Discoveries and Inventions

1. discovery
2. discovery
3. discovery
4. discovery
5. discovery
6. invention
7. invention

Page 34, Intriguing Inventions

1. a
2. c
3. b
4. d
5. b
6. c
7. a
8. d

Page 38, Posttest

1. b
2. a
3. a
4. d
5. c
6. a
7. c
8. d
9. d
10. a. D
    b. I
    c. I
    d. D

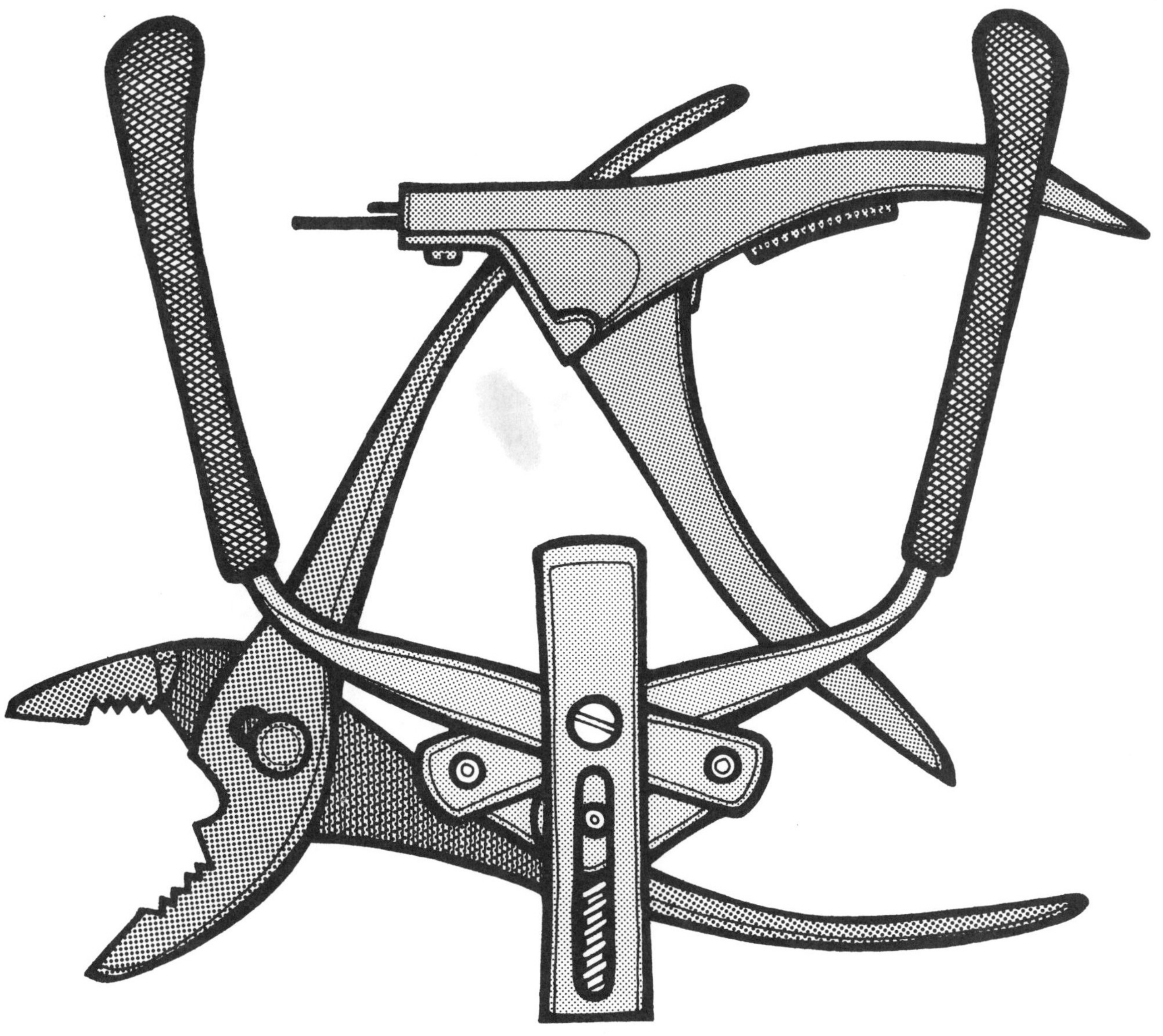

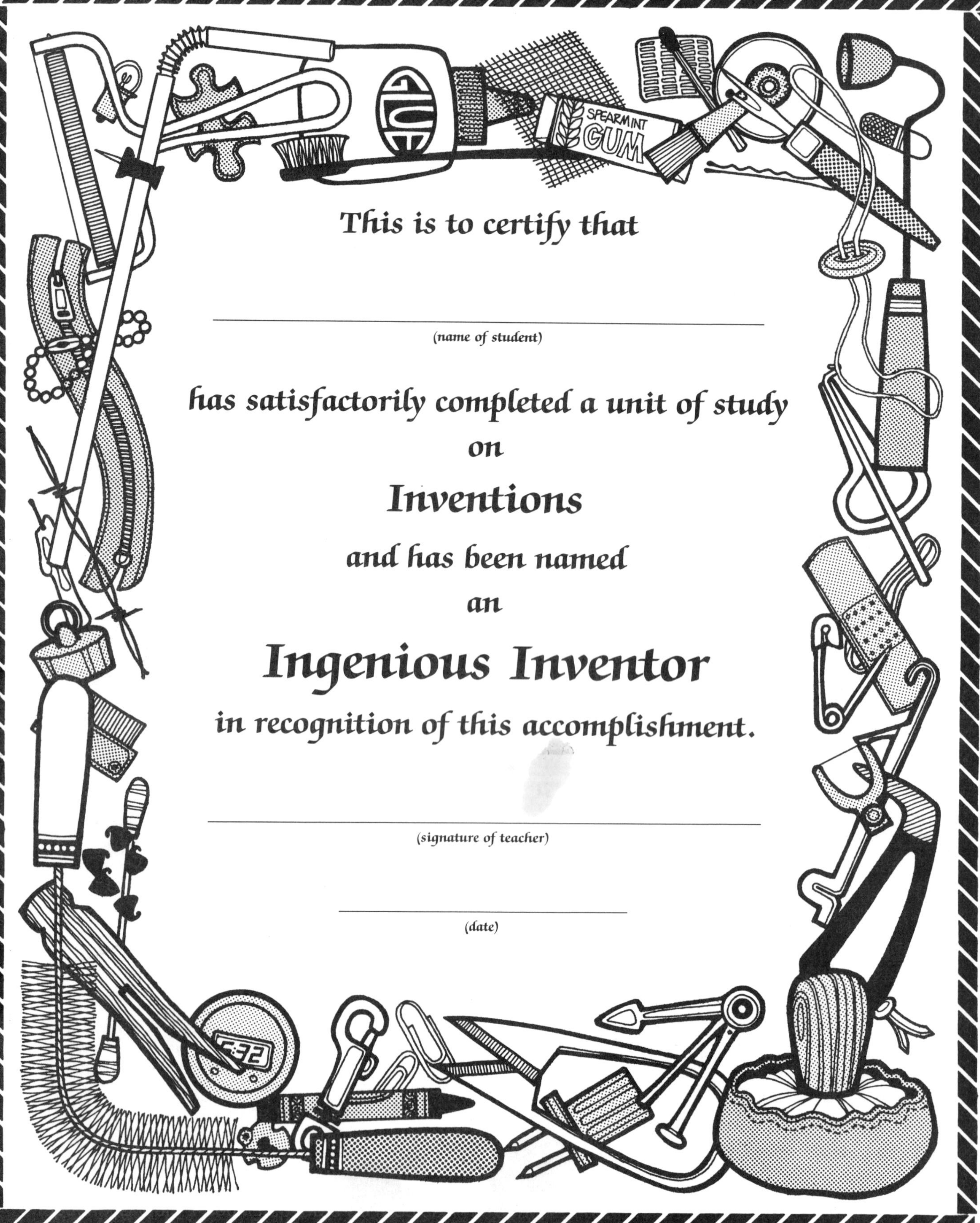

This is to certify that

____
(name of student)

has satisfactorily completed a unit of study
on

Inventions

and has been named
an

Ingenious Inventor

in recognition of this accomplishment.

____
(signature of teacher)

____
(date)